Jenny Lind and Her Listening Cat

By FRANCES CAVANAH

Illustrations by Paul Frame

SCHOLASTIC BOOK SERVICES

NEW YORK • TORONTO • LONDON • AUCKLAND • SYDNEY

4th printing .... September 1970

Printed in the U.S.A.

CONTENTS

You may want to read another book by the same author:

THEY LIVED IN THE WHITE HOUSE

A New Home

JENNY LIND was setting the table for supper. When she paused before the cracked mirror on the wall, a thin, plain-looking eight-year-old girl looked back at her. Her honey-colored hair hung in curls on either side of her face. Her eyes were blue-gray. But her nose was too broad, her mouth too big for her to be called pretty.

For an instant she continued to stare into the mirror, which reflected the shabby room and a door leading to the outer hall. The door had opened. A handsome man stood there. She whirled around and ran into his arms.

"Papa, Papa! Dear Papa!" she shouted.

Herr Lind lifted her off her feet and kissed her. He rubbed his moustache against her cheek and made it tickle.

"Oh, Papa," she whispered, her face pressed against his shoulder. "I wish you wouldn't ever go away again."

Fru Lind had heard the commotion and came in from the kitchen.

"Well, Niclas Jonas Lind," she said, "it's about time that you got here."

Her words sounded cross, but she was smiling. She seemed almost as pleased as Jenny.

"I came as soon as I received your letter," he replied. "Is there anything wrong, my dear? What did you want to see me about?"

"Time enough for that" — Fru Lind glanced at Jenny — "after the child is asleep."

Supper was a jolly meal, but meals were always jolly when Herr Lind was at home. Jenny and her mother lived in Stockholm, Sweden, and sometimes her father found work close by. More often he found positions in other towns, but no position lasted very long.

Fru Lind kept a school for girls in her dingy little flat, and it was she who had to pay the rent and buy the groceries. She often complained about how hard she had to work, but tonight she seemed happy. After the supper dishes were done, she brought out her guitar.

"Now, Niclas," she suggested, "let us have some music."

Jenny loved to hear her father sing. He sang many of the old Swedish folk songs, but his favorites were by the beloved Swedish poet, Karl Bellman. Jenny leaned against him. She hoped that he would sing the song about going fishing. It began with words addressed to a girl named Amaryllis, but Herr Lind sometimes substituted Jenny's name, and she liked that. He looked at her with a teasing smile.

> Up, Jenny — Jenny! Wake, little sweeting!
> Clouds are all fleeting,
> Cool the air.

See how the glowing
Rainbow, its flowing
Colors bestowing,
Makes all fair. . . .

Herr Lind slipped an arm around his daughter's waist.

"You sing with me," he whispered.

Jenny's eyes glowed. Her voice was sweet and high, each note like a little golden bell blending with her father's rich baritone.

Come, then, embark and sing with me sweetly!
Love rules completely
In our breast.
Winds that would harm us
Cannot alarm us,
Love still can charm us,
Make us blest.

Song followed song, until Jenny's mother decided it was high time Jenny was in bed. Her father came in to kiss her good night.

"I won't be here when you wake up," he said. "But remember . . ." He leaned closer and sang the words again:

Love still can charm us,
Make us blest.

Jenny was saying the words to herself as she dropped off to sleep.

She awoke some time later, hearing her own name. Her parents were talking in the next room, their voices raised in anger. Jenny put her hands over her ears, but the voices grew louder.

"I am giving up the flat," Fru Lind was saying. "The school does not pay for itself, and I must make a living in some other way. This chance to teach the children in a private family comes at just the right time."

"What about Jenny?" asked Herr Lind. "This position as governess you speak of is in another town. It is a hundred and fifty miles from Stockholm."

"I have been trying to tell you," Fru Lind snapped. "I have answered an advertisement in the Stockholm newspaper. Listen to this."

There was a rustling sound as she turned the pages.

"Here it is," she announced. "'A childless couple wish a child to take care of.' What do you think of that? Nothing about paying for her room and board. Why, this may not cost me a single krona."

"But what do you know about these people?" Niclas Lind protested.

"Nothing yet, but I have answered their advertisement, and I should hear from them by tomorrow. Anyway, it is the only thing to do. I can't take a gawky eight-year-old child with me into this new position."

Fru Lind broke off abruptly. "Niclas, did you leave that bedroom door open?"

He got up and closed the door, but it was a long time before Jenny went to sleep again. She did not want to go among strangers, and she was frightened by the thought of another change. Her short life had been a series of changes. As a very little girl, she had lived in the country with a couple whom her mother had paid to take care of her. When she was four, she had come home to stay with Mama, who was very busy and often very cross. But for a while she had had Mormor — her mother's mother. This kind, understanding grandmother, Fru Tengmark, was the person she loved more than anyone. Then Mormor had gone to live at the Stockholm Widows' Home. Jenny had visited her several times, but it was not the same.

And now Mama was deserting her. Who were these strange people that Fru Lind was talking about? A childless couple, she had said. Did that mean they did not like children? If she went to stay with them, would she ever see Mama or Papa again?

Would she ever see Mormor? Jenny dug her fists into the bedclothes and buried her face in the pillow. She did not want anyone to hear her crying.

Resolutely she dried her eyes. She began to sing under her breath the song she had sung earlier in the evening. Everything always seemed all right when she could sing:

> Love still can charm us,
> Make us blest.

Kisse Katt

THE NEXT MORNING at breakfast Jenny toyed with her wooden spoon. Her mother seemed worried.

"Eat your egg, Jenny," she said; then she added, "Were you listening last night?"

"I didn't mean to listen, Mama."

Fru Lind sighed.

"Did you hear what I was telling Papa?"

Jenny kept her eyes on her wooden plate.

"You said that I was going to live with strangers."

"Well, nothing is really settled yet. Perhaps today I'll have an answer to my letter."

There was no school that day, and after Fru Lind had departed on an errand, Jenny was left alone. She wandered through the narrow rooms, which suddenly seemed more attractive now that she knew she might have to leave them. They were her home. She turned her face away when she passed the corner where a good-sized switch was always left standing. After feeling the sting of that switch, Jenny usually set her lips in a thin line and refused to obey whatever order it was Fru Lind had given her. She knew that she was being stubborn, but she could not seem to help it. Why, she would do anything for Mama, she thought indignantly, if only Mama would love her.

She sat down at the piano, her hands looking very small against the black and white keys. She began to play the notes of a fanfare that she had heard a bugler play when she was only four years old. She would never forget that bugler. When she closed her eyes, she could still see him marching down the street at the head of a military band. She remembered exactly how he had raised his bugle to his lips and sounded the notes that set every nerve atingle.

Jenny, rushing to the piano, had picked out each note she had heard, not realizing her grandmother was listening. How proud Fru Tengmark had been!

"Mark my words," she had told Jenny's mother, "that child will be a great comfort and joy to you. Someday she will bring you help."

Jenny had never forgotten that fanfare. Now she sat down at the piano and played it again.

The door opened and Fru Lind came in.

"I have an answer to my letter," she said. "You can

never guess the name of the couple that wants a child. None other than Herr Andersson and his wife."

"Herr Andersson?" asked Jenny.

"You must have seen them when we went to call on

Mormor. He is the steward in charge at the Widows' Home."

Jenny could hardly believe the good news.

"Oh, am I to live at the Widows' Home? With Mormor?"

Fru Lind did not answer her question.

"Fru Andersson remembers you," she said, "even if you do not remember her. She never had any children of her own, and she says she will enjoy taking care of a *lillen* [little one]. Nor does she expect pay. It seems that I am to have some good fortune at last, and I can leave for my new position with a clear conscience."

The next few days passed in a blur of happiness. Fru Lind was busy — too busy even to scold. The school had to be closed. Arrangements must be made to give up the flat. Clothes for both of them had to be washed and ironed, and Jenny helped. On her last afternoon in her old home, she carefully folded her neatly patched and darned little dresses and packed them in a carpetbag. After supper, she and her mother set out for the Widows' Home.

Always before, they had walked. But Jenny's carpetbag was heavy, and this evening they went in style. Fru Lind hired a carriage, and Jenny settled back against the cushions to enjoy her first ride. The horse's hoofs seemed to beat a glad tattoo on the cobblestones as they left behind the narrow street where she had lived for the past four years. Some of the streets through which they passed were mere lanes, darkened by tall houses on either side. But as they came nearer Küngstradgarden, the King's Park, there was a feeling of space and light and brightness. Jenny saw many carriages besides their own. Elegantly dressed ladies sat beside elegant gentlemen. Other couples walked in the park beneath the trees, the men flourishing their canes. From a café on the corner came the gay strains of an orchestra.

Jenny was looking straight ahead. She could see the big handsome building where her grandmother, Fru Tengmark, lived. It had once been a palace, built for a Swedish nobleman, but was now a home for widows, once well-to-do, who could no longer afford to live in houses of their own. When the coachman reached the gate, he drew rein before a small lodge just inside the grounds. He climbed down from the high driver's seat and held out his hand to help Fru Lind from the carriage. She paid him his fare.

"Come, Jenny," she said. "We are here."

"Mormor doesn't live in this little house," Jenny protested. "She hasn't moved, has she?"

"Of course not. This is the lodge where the steward lives."

Jenny's lip trembled. "You said I was going to stay with Mormor."

"I said nothing of the sort," Fru Lind replied. "The Widows' Home is for old ladies. You can't stay there. You should know that."

She was interrupted by the opening of a door, and Herr and Fru Andersson hurried out to greet them. Jenny reluctantly climbed down from the carriage and made a curtsy.

"Welcome, Jenny child!" said Fru Andersson kindly. "I have seen you several times when you came to visit Fru Tengmark."

Her husband laughed. "Ah, but Jenny has not seen *us*," he said. "She had eyes for no one except for that precious grandmother of hers."

Jenny curtsied again. "May I go to see Mormor now?"

"No, child," Herr Andersson told her. "All of the old ladies are in bed and, I dare say, sound asleep by now."

"Except the one who is ill," said his wife. She turned back to Fru Lind. "It is unfortunate that you arrive tonight. The doctor is coming to see one of our old ladies, and we must go to her. Will you help your *lillen* to get settled? She is to have the room to the left of the front door."

"I haven't much time," Fru Lind objected. "I must leave early in the morning to take my new position."

Herr Andersson drew her aside and spoke in a low voice. Jenny thought she heard the words "Fru Tengmark." Then he and his wife hurried up the path to the Widows' Home. Her mother opened the door of the lodge.

Jenny's room faced the street and looked out over the King's Park. It was a small, neat room, with a table, a chair, and a big chest all painted blue. The bed, like many beds in Sweden, looked like a long box, set against one wall. In the daytime it could be closed and used as a seat. Tonight it was open, with a pretty blue-and-white quilt folded back at one corner. The linen sheet beneath it was snowy white.

"Now, get undressed," said Fru Lind, "and don't forget to say your prayers."

Jenny tugged at the buttons on her bodice, but said nothing. She was afraid she would cry if she tried to talk. She was going to live with strangers after all.

"You must remember to be a good girl," her mother went on. "If you are stubborn, Fru Andersson may not be willing to keep you. What would happen to you then I am sure I don't know, for I shall be far away."

Her lips brushed Jenny's cheek, and she was gone.

Jenny slipped into her nightgown and knelt by the window. The sky had faded to a faint gray. A summer night in Sweden is never wholly dark, and she could see the outlines of the Widows' Home through the trees. She wondered what Herr Andersson had said about Fru Tengmark. Was she the lady who was ill?

"Oh, dear God," Jenny finished her prayer, "please make Mormor well again."

Looking down the street, she could make out the tall steeple of St. Jacob's Church. In the opposite direction she could see the lights of the café. The orchestra was playing, but the music no longer sounded gay. There were fewer carriages on the street, but people still strolled in the park. Several couples walked arm in arm. A little boy rode on his father's shoulders as they hurried toward their home. Beside him walked his sister, clinging to her mother's hand. Everyone had someone else.

Everyone except Jenny.

There was a slight noise beneath her window — a soft, inquiring mew. Jenny glanced down and saw a small gray cat looking up at her.

"Why, it's a kitty-cat! A little *kisse katt,*" she said. "Kisse Katt, do you belong to Fru Andersson?"

"Meow!" the kitten replied.

Even in the fading light, Jenny could see that it was very thin. It probably was a stray and belonged to no one. She leaned as far out of the window as she could and put down her hand. The kitten stood on its small gray haunches and tried to sniff her fingers. It could not quite reach them.

"You wait there, Kisse Katt," she said in a low voice. "I am coming out to get you."

As she groped her way through the dark hall, she bumped into a table, but there was no one in the house to hear. There was no one to see her open the door. The kitten was waiting on the doorstep, and it began to purr when Jenny picked it up.

"Oh, Kisse Katt," she said, cuddling it against her neck. "I never had a pet before. If Fru Andersson . . ."

Only then did she stop to think that she should ask permission. But Fru Andersson was not there to ask, and Jenny wondered uneasily if she liked cats. At that moment Kisse Katt snuggled his head into the hollow of her hand and gave a piteous little meow. She could feel his heart thumping, and her own heart was thumping very fast. She couldn't — she simply couldn't — put this bedraggled little bunch of fur back on the doorstep. She carried him into her room.

"Don't you worry, Kisse Katt," she whispered. "I'll take care of you."

Again the kitten began to purr. It was a reassuring kind of purr. He seemed to be trying to tell her that he intended to take care of her.

Bell on a Blue Ribbon

WHEN JENNY AWOKE the following morning, the sunshine pouring through the window seemed to bathe the room in a golden light. It was a pretty room — much nicer than the dark corner in which she had been used to sleeping. She yawned and stretched her toes under the blue-and-white quilt.

It was then she felt something stirring in the crook of her arm. A small furry head was thrust against her chin.

"Why, Kisse Katt, I had forgotten about you!"

"Meow!" The kitten reached out a pink tongue and licked her hand.

"Oo-oo-h!" Jenny pretended to shiver.

She had never known that anything so soft as a kitten could have such a rough tongue. She placed the

little cat on the quilt in front of her, so that she might get a better look at him. He was gray, except for four white paws and a white spot in front. In daylight, he seemed even thinner and more bedraggled than he had the night before. With a slap of his paw, he thrust Jenny's hand aside and set to work to make himself presentable.

First, he dampened a white paw with a pink tongue and ran it over his face. He preened his whiskers. He licked his hind legs. He turned and twisted to reach his back. His tail was curled around him, and he licked that. His tongue had become a washcloth and comb and brush combined, and already he was beginning to look like a different cat. His gray fur shone. The patch of white on his chest reminded Jenny of Papa's white shirt front. And when he finished with his front paws, they looked like two neat white gloves. Having cleaned himself to his satisfaction, he snuggled down again in the crook of Jenny's arm.

"Why, you are beautiful!" Jenny exclaimed. "But so thin. I shall give you part of my breakfast. I'll ask Fru Andersson — "

She gave a gasp of dismay. She had forgotten Fru Andersson. What was the steward's wife going to say when she learned that Jenny had a cat and had taken it to bed with her? She knew what her mother would have said — and done. Perhaps she would be told she had to leave. Perhaps the kitten would be driven off to starve. Jenny wondered if she could hide him.

The door of her room was opening, and she started to thrust her pet under the covers. But that was not Jenny Lind's way. Whatever the consequences, she always told the truth.

"Good morning, Jenny," said Fru Andersson. "Breakfast will be ready soon. Why, what — "

She stopped in surprise and walked over to the bed.

"What have we here?" she asked.

"I call him Kisse Katt," said Jenny in a small voice. "I know I shouldn't have let him in without asking first. But he was crying under my window last night, and he seemed so lonely."

"Were you lonely too?"

Jenny nodded.

"Take a lonely kitten and a lonely little girl, put them together — and what happens?"

Jenny looked up wonderingly. "Then neither of them is lonely any more."

"Exactly." Fru Andersson was smiling.

"You mean I may keep Kisse Katt?"

"Well, I don't like lonely cats, and I don't want any lonely little girls around my house. Suppose you ask your grandmother. If she says you may keep the kitten, it will be all right with me."

"Is Mormor all right?" asked Jenny anxiously.

"To be sure she is. One of the other old ladies, Fru Larsen, had to have the doctor last night, but she feels better now. She and all the rest are waiting to see you."

"I may see Mormor? Today?"

"Today and every day. My husband was telling your mother so last night, but you will have your meals in the lodge with us. Now, *lillen,* you must get ready for breakfast. As for Kisse Katt" — she leaned down and stroked the thin sides — "I think he will enjoy a bowl of good warm milk."

Jenny jumped out of bed and hurried across the room to the chair where her clothes lay neatly folded. The kitten pounced, attracted by the movement of her bare feet on the wide floor boards. When Jenny squealed, he was convinced that she was playing. He reached out a dainty paw to catch the long white stocking she started to put on. He made a flying leap and clung to her striped skirt, swinging back and forth like a small, furry trapeze performer. Jenny was laughing as she loosened his claws and carried him out into the kitchen.

Fru Andersson stood at the tile stove, stirring something in a copper pan.

"Welcome, Kisse Katt," she said. "Your breakfast is ready."

He did not wait for a second invitation. He wriggled out of Jenny's arms and dashed over to the yellow bowl in the corner. His pink tongue lapped up the white milk. He sat back on his haunches and licked his chops as he looked up at Fru Andersson.

"Meow!" he said.

"You *were* hungry, weren't you?" she replied, as she filled his bowl a second time. "I only hope that Jenny likes porridge as much as you like milk."

Jenny sat down at the clean-scrubbed table in the sunny corner by the window. Just outside she could see Herr Andersson weeding a flower bed, and the dahlias made a bright-red splotch of color against the green grass. Fru Andersson poured herself a cup of coffee and took a chair opposite Jenny. Her round, fat face was one big smile, and Jenny was fascinated by the way both her chins wobbled when she talked.

"We never had any children of our own," she explained. "We were much pleased, my good husband and myself, when Fru Lind answered our advertisement. We had seen you when you visited your grandmother, and Fru Tengmark has talked about you every day. We all hope, *lillen,* that you will like it here."

Jenny felt a sudden warm glow. It was a good feeling to know that she was wanted.

When she finished her breakfast, she rose and made a little curtsy.

"Thank you for the food, Fru Andersson. Thank you, *Tant.*"

In Sweden it was the custom for a younger person to call an older woman "Aunt" when they became good friends. Fru Andersson looked pleased, and she smoothed a lock of honey-colored hair back from the white forehead.

"Now, suppose you take Kisse Katt to show your grandmother," she suggested.

Meanwhile Fru Tengmark, very neat in a crisp white cap and kerchief over a block dress, was waiting in her sitting room at the Widows' Home. Although thin and slightly stooped, she did not seem frail. The blue-gray eyes were faded but her glance was sharp and straightforward. Again and again she looked up from her sewing, and her face brightened when she heard light, running footsteps coming down the hall.

Jenny stood in the doorway, holding the gray kitten. She set the kitten down on the floor and ran into her grandmother's arms.

"Oh, Mormor, Mormor," she cried, "am I really going to see you any time I want to?"

"Yes, Jenny, the good Lord be praised!" Fru Tengmark could hardly keep a quaver out of her voice. "We shall be together every day, and we can talk and play games, and I shall tell you stories from the Bible. I shall teach you to sew, if you wish. And you shall sing for me as you used to."

"May Kisse Katt come too?"

"Kisse Katt?"

Jenny looked down at her shoes. In slow, halting words she told of the kitten's arrival the night before and how much they already loved each other.

"Fru Andersson says I may keep him if it is all right with you," she finished.

As though he knew he was being talked about, Kisse

Katt padded across the floor. He rubbed against Fru Tengmark's ankles. It was easy to see that he liked her. But did Mormor like Kisse Katt? Or was she going to scold Jenny for taking the cat in without asking permis-

sion? Mormor's scoldings were always gentle, but Jenny loved her too much not to want to please her.

At last Fru Tengmark spoke. "He is a very nice pussy. With good food and good care, I am sure that he will grow into a handsome cat. But you love birds so much, Jenny. You know that cats catch birds."

Jenny stared at her pet in dismay. "Kisse Katt would never be that wicked," she protested. "Besides, I'll teach him not to."

"He would not know that he was being wicked, and perhaps . . ." Fru Tengmark hesitated. "Well, perhaps you *can* teach him. I have something I think will help."

In her workbasket she found a small silver bell that she had been saving for Jenny. She shook it gently and it gave out a soft, tinkly sound.

"Not as pretty, of course, as the little bell in your throat," she said.

Jenny remembered how sometimes Mormor used to tease her when she sang. She said it sounded exactly as though Jenny kept a bell hidden in her throat.

"We shall tie this bell around Kisse Katt's neck," Fru Tengmark explained. "Then the birds will hear him coming and fly away before he can catch them."

She reached into her workbasket again.

"I have a nice ribbon here some place. Ah, here it is."

She picked up a needle and thread, and quickly sewed the bell in the middle of the narrow blue band. Kisse Katt jumped into her lap and reached out an inquisitive paw. He batted the bell back and forth, until Mormor held it up out of his reach. Then she looped the ribbon around his neck and tied the ends in a big bow.

Jenny fluffed out the bow and tried it over Kisse Katt's right ear. She tried it over his left ear. She pulled it around so that it looked like a tie for his white shirt front. She decided that he was handsome whichever way he wore it.

"My beautiful, beautiful Kisse Katt!" she said.

She made the words into a little song. Kisse Katt blinked his green eyes and patted her neck with a soft white paw. Was there, indeed, a silver bell hidden in her throat? he seemed to ask.

"Jenny," said Fru Tengmark, "my friends all want to see you. Will you come back when we have our coffee hour this afternoon and sing for us?"

"I will! Oh, I will!"

Jenny gave her grandmother another big hug. She could always sing when she was happy. And she was very happy now.

A Song for a Cat

AS THE WEEKS PASSED, Jenny seemed to grow happier day by day. Herr and Fru Andersson were always kind. She saw her grandmother any time she wished, and the other ladies at the Widows' Home looked forward to her visits. They were reminded of the days when their own children had been young, or of granddaughters whom they seldom saw, and they liked to hear her sing. Sometimes as they sat in the afternoon sunshine, their hands busy with knitting or some piece of needlework, they all sang together.

Jenny especially liked the old Swedish and Norwegian folk songs. Fru Larsen, one of Mormor's friends, had been born in Norway. She had come to

Sweden to live after her marriage, and had attended the opera in Stockholm many times. She taught Jenny some new songs, and used interesting new words. Girls who, like Jenny, had high voices, sang "in soprano," she said. Girls with low voices sang "in alto." Afterward, in her room at the lodge, Jenny used the same words in talking to her cat.

"Why don't we have a duet?" she asked him one afternoon. "You can purr in alto, while I sing in soprano."

She was sitting by the window, holding Kisse Katt in her lap. Down the street, the tall steeple of St. Jacob's Church was outlined against the sky. Across the way in the King's Park some children were gathered around a peep-show man. Each, in turn, peeped through a hole in his box. Inside the box was a magnifying glass that made the picture they saw look very real. It must have been a funny picture, from the way they laughed.

Jenny did not seem to hear them. She had forgotten the children. She had forgotten that there were people tramping past her window. Her eyes were closed. She was seeing a lonely hillside and a herdsman driving a herd of cows home for the night. She began to sing his song.

The sun is setting behind the hills,
The shadows are lengthening;
The night will soon close in
And hold us in its lap.

The pot is on the fire
And to the Alp I wend my way.

Kisse Katt closed his eyes and purred a soft accompaniment. Jenny's next notes — thin, but sweet and clear — sounded like an echo from a distant mountainside:

Hoah, hoah, hoah!
Come hither, come hither, come hither!
Hoah, hoah, hoah!

She had started another stanza when she noticed that several people had gathered outside her window. She broke off in surprise.

"Who was that singing?" a woman in a big bonnet and wide skirts asked her husband. "It could not have been that little girl."

"Indeed it was!" her husband replied. "It was the little girl singing to her cat."

Jenny buried her fingers in her pet's gray fur.

"Why are all those people staring?" she whispered. "Is it because they like to hear me sing?"

The wonder of it, the thought that she had given pleasure to others, brought a flush to her cheeks. "Anyway, *you* like to hear me," she went on talking to her pet. "My dear little listening cat!"

Kisse Katt tucked his paws under him, purring a little louder. He kept on purring, even after the people outside the window had passed on down the street.

After that, Jenny often sat in the window and sang to her cat, but with the coming of cold weather the window had to be kept closed. Winter days are short in Sweden, and by three o'clock in the afternoon it was

usually so dark that the candles had to be lit. Fru Tengmark was teaching Jenny to sew, and she sat close to the flickering flame to make sure that her stitches were neat and even. They were strong, too — so strong that they never came out — and Jenny was proud when Mormor said she sewed almost as well as she sang.

Kisse Katt not only listened to Jenny sing; he had his duties, too. He did not wear his bell indoors, and he poked his pink nose into every corner of the Widows' Home, to make sure there were no mice. He was growing bigger every day, and by spring he was fully grown.

As always, people throughout Sweden rejoiced in the return of summer. The season seemed all the more wonderful because it was so brief. The sun shone from three o'clock in the morning until nine at night. The willow trees in the park were green again, their delicate leaves showing like fragile lace against the sky, and the lilac bushes were a mass of purple bloom. The birds returned, and Jenny tried to imitate them when they sang. She and her grandmother spent nearly every afternoon in the garden.

Of course, Kisse Katt had to wear his bell again, but he did not seem to mind. He liked the sunshine, and he found it great fun to chase his shadow. Sometimes he hid behind a bush, and Jenny had to hunt for him. Fru Tengmark would smile as she sat under a tree, her hands busy with her knitting. She was thinking how different Jenny looked. Although still small for her age, Jenny's cheeks were as pink as the roses in Herr Andersson's garden.

Hardly less remarkable was the change in Kisse Katt. It was hard to realize that Jenny's handsome pet with the sleek gray coat was the bedraggled kitten she had found crying beneath her window. Certainly no cat ever had a more comfortable home. Not only Fru Andersson, but several of the old ladies fed him tidbits. At night he slept at the foot of Jenny's bed — something her mother would never have permitted. He curled up on her lap when Mormor told her stories. And he had a big garden to play in.

However, there came an afternoon when he refused to play. Jenny offered him an extra bowl of milk. He took a few laps to be polite, then turned away. She tickled him behind the ears where usually he liked to be tickled. Instead of purring, he mewed in pain. Jenny picked him up tenderly and carried him over to her grandmother's chair.

"Kisse Katt must be sick." She blinked to keep back the tears. "Can't you make him well again?"

"No, *lillen,* but Kisse Katt knows what to do. If we leave him alone, he will slip away somewhere and rest until he feels better," Fru Tengmark assured her. "Besides, haven't you ever heard that a cat has nine lives?"

"Really?" Jenny asked.

"No, it is just an old superstition — something people say because cats are so smart about taking care of themselves. Still" — there was a twinkle in Mormor's eyes — "if any cat can manage it, I am sure that our Kisse Katt can. Don't worry about him. He will soon be well again."

Kisse Katt made a noise deep in his throat. He was doing his best to purr, but when Jenny tried to cuddle him closer, he twisted out of her arms and hid under a bush.

She did not see him again for several days.

Then one morning he was back, his old playful self again. Taking him in her arms, Jenny rushed up the path to the Widows' Home. She sang every step of the way.

"I declare," said Fru Tengmark, "that silver bell in your throat is growing sweeter every day."

"Kisse Katt's purr is improving, too," said Jenny. "Just listen to him, Mormor."

Now that it was summer, the windows were open again to the soft breezes, and nearly every day Jenny sat at the window sill and sang while Kisse Katt listened. Often a crowd gathered outside, but Jenny did not think there was anything remarkable about that. She loved to sing, and she was glad people liked to listen.

Early one afternoon that autumn, she saw a tall dark-eyed girl staring up at her. The girl's red plaid shawl had slipped unnoticed from her shoulders.

"*Brava! Brava!*" she cried when the song was finished.

Then, hastily gathering up her shawl, she hurried away.

Did the young woman not like the way she sang? Jenny wondered. Yet she had shouted "*Brava!*"

Jenny glanced down at Kisse Katt as he lay stretched out on her lap. From the way he curled and uncurled his paws, she knew that he was pleased, and she leaned closer to listen to him purr. He purred all evening. Surely something nice was about to happen, Jenny decided as she climbed into bed. The bells of St. Jacob's Church were pealing softly as she dropped off to sleep.

Some time later she awakened, aware of a strange brightness. She crept to the window, her eyes still heavy with sleep. At first she thought that the King's Park must be on fire. Then she saw that the fire was in the sky. She blinked, and the fire became streamers of light — blue, yellow, green, pink, crimson — stretching across the horizon like a gigantic rainbow. These bright bands shone steadily at first and then began to tremble and quiver against the darker curtain of the sky.

Like other Swedish children, Jenny knew about the aurora borealis, that luminous display of flickering lights often seen in the skies of northern countries. But never before had she seen northern lights of such awe-inspiring beauty. She remembered a line from one of the Bible stories Mormor had told her: "And God said, Let there be light: and there was light."

Finally she crept, shivering, back to bed. But she found that the glowing ribbons of light still shone for her. She had only to close her eyes to see them again.

A Letter

JENNY COULD HARDLY WAIT to tell her grandmother about the northern lights — to share with her the wonder she had felt when the colored streamers flamed in the sky.

"Yes, I was awake," Fru Tengmark replied. "Many times I have seen them during my long life, but never were they more brilliant than last night."

Jenny closed her eyes.

"I can still see them, Mormor. I can see the sky on fire and the bright ribbons flashing. They are like a picture against my eyelids. Why is that?"

"One can always keep the memory of a lovely thing, Jenny. Memory is one of the good Lord's gifts to us."

"But I can see some things I never really saw," Jenny went on earnestly. "When I sing the song about the herdsman, I can *see* him driving his cows down the mountain. After a while I begin to feel I *am* the herdsman. Is that wrong?"

"No, *lillen*," her grandmother replied tenderly. "It only means that you understand the herdsman so well that you know how he thinks and how he feels. God has given you a beautiful voice. But you must never forget to *understand* and to feel, if you would sing songs that touch our hearts."

She reached into her pocket and brought out a letter.

"This is from your mother, Jenny. She is back and will be here to visit us this afternoon. In this letter she says that things did not go well in her new position, and she has rented another flat in Stockholm."

"Oh!"

Jenny wanted very much to see her mother, but an old fear clutched her heart.

"Mormor," she asked, "do you suppose Mama will love me this time?"

"She *does* love you." Fru Tengmark spoke firmly, but her eyes were troubled. "You must know how hard she works for you."

"I . . . I know she does."

"Life has not been easy for your mother," Fru Tengmark went on. "When she seems cross, it is because she is so tired. We all have faults, remember."

"Even Kisse Katt?"

Fru Tengmark had to laugh.

"Even Kisse Katt. He probably would be outdoors this minute, trying to catch a bird, if he did not wear that bell around his neck. But don't try to change the subject. Even my darling Jenny can be very stubborn sometimes."

"Yes, and it is wicked of me, I suppose," Jenny admitted. "Sometimes I do things that I *know* will make Mama angry. But it is so much easier to be good when people love me."

"Of course, and that is why you must love your mother. Put yourself in her place. Try to understand her, just as you understand the herdsman when you sing his song."

"I'll try. I truly will, and I'll wear the new dress you made me. I can't be pretty, but Mama always likes me to look nice."

"Ah, but you are pretty when you smile," her grandmother assured her.

Jenny felt more like crying than smiling, as she walked back to the lodge. After her midday meal, she went to her room and put on her new dress. Her pet rubbed against her ankles, purring in his most approving manner. Jenny sat down by the window to wait, and it seemed that the time would never pass.

Kisse Katt, without waiting to be asked, jumped up in her lap. He arched his head in the hollow of her hand, as though he knew that she was worried. She did not need to speak her thoughts out loud; even when she just thought them to herself, he seemed to understand.

The door opened and Fru Andersson looked in.

"Jenny," she said, "you are wanted at the Widows' Home. Your mother has come — your mother, and someone else."

Jenny raced up the path, Kisse Katt bounding after her. She was quite out of breath by the time she reached her grandmother's sitting room. Fru Lind herself opened the door. There was a frown between her eyes, but Fru Tengmark looked up from her knitting to smile reassuringly.

There was still another person in the room. A dark-eyed young woman in a red plaid shawl was pointing to Jenny as she talked.

"Yes, she is the one — the *lilla flicka,* the little girl with the honey-colored hair."

Jenny, feeling bewildered, edged closer to her grandmother. Kisse Katt stared with wide green eyes at the visitor. He seemed to recognize her. Certainly Jenny did. It was the girl who had stood outside her window the afternoon before, listening to her sing, and had then hurried away so abruptly.

"This young woman," Fru Tengmark explained, "is the maid of Mademoiselle Lundberg, a dancer at the Royal Opera House. She brings us a letter from Mademoiselle, who was under the impression that your mother lived at the lodge."

Jenny curtsied. She knew that the Swedish king, once called Bernadotte, had been born in France. He spoke only French, and many other people in Stockholm liked to use French words. Young ladies were often called *Mademoiselle,* not *Froken,* the Swedish word for "Miss." Married women were called *Madame* instead of *Fru.* Gentlemen were sometimes known as *Monsieur,* not *Herr.*

The maid returned Jenny's curtsy. In her eagerness, the words seemed to tumble over one another, as she went on to explain.

"Yesterday afternoon," she said, "my mistress sent me on an errand, and then she scolded me because I was late in returning. What could have kept me so long? she asked. I answered, 'What, indeed, but the *flicka* who sings so divinely that I could not force myself to move away.' Mademoiselle Lundberg said that was no excuse. I told her if she had heard the *flicka* sing, she would think I had excuse enough."

The maid paused for breath.

"My mistress was so interested that she wrote a letter and asked me to bring it to the lodge by the gate. The fat lady I had seen there — I thought perhaps she was the *flicka's* mother. She said I would find you here. How fortunate, Fru Lind, that you should have come for a visit at this time."

Again Fru Lind frowned.

"I do not approve of dancers," she said.

The maid drew herself up proudly.

"My mistress is a very lovely lady — a beautiful

dancer, a great artist. Ah, I beseech you, take your daughter to see her."

Jenny laid a hand on her mother's knee.

"Mama," she asked, "does someone want to hear me sing?"

"Yes," said Fru Lind shortly. "Mademoiselle Lundberg has asked that we call on her this afternoon. But I do not think that we should go."

"Why not, daughter?" asked Fru Tengmark. "It can do no harm. If Mademoiselle wants to hear our Jenny sing, we should give her that pleasure."

"Very well."

Fru Lind folded the letter and put it in her pocket.

"Run down to the lodge, Jenny, and get your shawl and bonnet."

Jenny's face was flushed. She threw her arms around her grandmother's neck and kissed the withered cheek. She laid her hand on Kisse Katt's head.

"I'll tell you all about it when I get back," she promised.

The Royal Opera House

MADEMOISELLE LUNDBERG was not like anyone Jenny Lind had ever seen before. She wore a lavender embroidered bodice over wide-spreading skirts, and there was a faint scent of violets in the room. Jenny did not know that it was perfume, but she liked it. She wrinkled her nose and sniffed. For some reason the lovely dancer seemed amused, and Jenny suddenly felt shy and awkward. When she was asked to sing, she looked down at the floor.

Mademoiselle reached out her hand.

"Do not be afraid," she said kindly. "You sing for your cat, so why not for me? Just one song!"

Jenny closed her eyes. She seemed to see a lonely

herdsman driving his herd of cows down a mountainside. She took a deep breath. She sang the old folk song, which ended with the words:

> Come hither, come hither, come hither!
> *Hoah, hoah, hoah!*

Only then did she dare to look at Mademoiselle. The dancer was crying.

"Ah, *lillen,* sing to me again," she begged. "Sing to me again!"

So Jenny sang a second song. She could not understand why the beautiful lady should keep on crying. Yet at the end of each song she asked for another. Finally she dried her eyes and turned to Fru Lind.

"Madame," she said, using the French form of address, "you must have your daughter educated for the stage."

Fru Lind was shocked.

"Indeed not," she said. "We may be poor, but I would never let a child of mine go on the stage."

Mademoiselle looked annoyed, but she knew many people in that year of 1829 did not approve of the theater. She tried to keep her temper.

"Your daughter is a genius — she has great talent," she went on. "A voice like hers must not be wasted. You will, at least, allow her to take singing lessons, will you not?"

"We have no money for music lessons."

"Ah, but I know someone who may be willing to teach her — not for money, but because her voice is so beautiful. Herr Croelius, the singing master at the Royal Opera House, is my friend. I shall write him a letter."

She sat down at the writing desk and drew a sheet of paper toward her. The scratching of her quill pen across the paper was the only sound in the room. When she finished the note, she handed it to Fru Lind.

"Be so good as to take this to Herr Croelius. All I ask is that you let him hear your daughter sing."

Jenny's thoughts were in a whirl as she followed her mother into a narrow, cobblestoned street. Mademoiselle had kissed her. She had assured her that the singing master was kind. Jenny was frightened at the idea of singing for him, yet even more frightened that she might not have the chance. Her mother, instead of walking in the direction of the Opera House, started across the King's Park toward the Widows' Home. Then, abruptly, she turned and began to walk in the opposite direction.

"Mama, are we going to see Herr Croelius?" Jenny asked.

Fru Lind, busy with her own thoughts, did not answer, and Jenny did not dare ask again. As usual, the park was crowded. She and her mother passed a milk-maid. This pretty young woman had two buckets, each hanging from one end of a bar she carried over her shoulders. Several people had stopped to buy milk from her. Farther on, everyone stepped aside when a column of the royal guard marched past. The king had commanded that each soldier wear a mustache, and most of the soldiers had real hair on their upper lips. A few of the younger men, however, had mustaches painted on, and Jenny could hardly keep from laughing. There was always something interesting to see in Stockholm.

It was a city built partly on several hilly islands. When Jenny and her mother came to Gustavus Adolphus Torg, the wide square on which the Opera House stood, they looked out over shifting waves. Sailboats, scudding before a brisk wind, passed almost at their feet. Sea gulls spread wide wings and rose with hoarse cries into the air. Close by, a long granite bridge, the Norrbro (North Bridge), led to the island known as Old Town. It was here that the city of Stockholm had been founded nearly six hundred years before. And it was here that the King of Sweden lived. Jenny could see his magnificent palace across the shining expanse of water.

Turning back toward the Opera House, she and her mother passed the statue of one of Sweden's earlier kings, Gustavus Adolphus, for whom the square was named. Her heart was beating fast as they approached the handsome stone Opera House. She glanced up at the heavy gray columns.

Her mother stopped short.

"I won't do it, Jenny. I won't take you into that wicked place."

"It doesn't look wicked," Jenny protested. "Oh, Mama, do let me sing for the singing master."

Fru Lind seemed to be trying to make up her mind. Finally, without another word, she mounted the steps, and Jenny followed. A few minutes later they were knocking at the door of a studio on the second floor. A man in a long black coat and a high white collar rose to greet them, and Fru Lind curtsied and handed him Mademoiselle Lundberg's letter. He put on his spectacles and read it carefully.

"Mademoiselle has asked that I listen to you sing," said Herr Croelius. "Would you like to try a song for me?"

He was kind, as Mademoiselle had said. But it was plain that he considered Jenny rather young to be taking up his time. She decided that she would sing something difficult — a song from an opera that Fru Larsen at the Widows' Home had taught her.

At the first note, Herr Croelius sat up straight. Fru Lind noticed his amazement, and she herself was surprised. She had no idea where Jenny had learned the song she was singing. She glanced at the singing master, curious about what he would say.

He said nothing at all. He took off his glasses and

wiped them. He rose, came over, and took both of Jenny's hands in his. There were tears in his eyes.

"Mademoiselle is right, *lillen,*" he told her. "Now I want Count Puke to hear you. Come with me."

The count was the head director of the theater, the music master explained as they walked down a long hall to another studio. He knocked on the door. When they entered, the count looked very cross. He had been trying out singers all that afternoon, and none of them had pleased him. He glanced at Fru Lind.

"Ah, Herr Croelius, have you brought me another who wants to sing? Another who thinks she is a prima donna?" he asked.

"It is my daughter who sings," said Fru Lind indignantly.

"That undersized child? Do you think I am conducting a nursery? This is the Royal Theater of Stockholm."

Jenny's lips were set in the same thin line as her mother's.

"I do not know what a prima donna is," she said, trying to keep her voice steady, "but I am eight years old. I'm *almost* nine."

At that, the count smiled a little.

"Even so," he said in a kinder tone, "you are too young, and I am a busy man. I do not have time to hear you sing."

Herr Croelius stepped forward.

"I, too, had doubts at first. But if *Monsieur le Comte*

will not hear the *flicka,* then I myself will teach her. I promise that one day she will astonish you."

"You think she is that good, do you?" the count asked. "All right, if I must listen to her, I suppose I must."

Jenny glanced nervously around the room, twisting the corner of her shawl. The count looked so bored that she was thoroughly frightened. But she was stubborn, too. She would show this man what she could do; she would sing the song from the opera again. She opened her mouth to begin, but no sound came. She swallowed hard. She tried once more, and this time her notes were sweet and pure and clear. By the end of her song, she forgot that she had ever been afraid.

It was the count's turn to be amazed, and his eyes were suspiciously moist. When Jenny finished, he walked over to the window and looked down on the square, now deep in shadow. He turned to Fru Lind.

"Have the child wait outside. I want to talk with you alone."

On the way back to the Widows' Home that evening, Fru Lind was plainly worried. Not until they reached the gate by the lodge did Jenny find the courage to ask a question.

"Didn't the count like the way I sang?"

"We shall talk about it in the morning," her mother replied. "I must have Mormor's advice. Now, run inside. I am sure Fru Andersson has your supper waiting for you."

When Jenny went to her room, she carefully folded her shawl and laid it in the top drawer of the blue painted chest. She was thinking of all the surprising things that had happened. Singing came naturally to her — as naturally as to the birds in Herr Andersson's garden. But that afternoon, frightened though she had been, she had made a surprising discovery. It was a discovery about herself.

Something soft and furry was rubbing against her ankles.

"Oh, Kisse Katt," said Jenny, "more than anything I want to sing. I mean I want to learn to sing better. I want to learn to really sing."

Askungen

"MORMOR," Jenny asked the next morning when she went to see her grandmother, "why do people cry when I sing?"

"As I told you yesterday, it is because you touch their hearts."

Jenny was puzzled. Kisse Katt, asleep on the sofa beside her, evidently decided that he was not getting enough attention. He climbed over on her lap, sat up on his gray haunches, raised a white paw, and patted the front of her white bodice.

Jenny giggled.

"The way Kisse Katt is trying to touch my heart?" she asked.

She knew better, of course. She knew what her grandmother really meant, because she remembered how she had felt about her pet when he first arrived. She was so sorry for the poor, half-starved kitten that she had wanted to help and protect him. He had touched her heart. Now, as he snuggled up against her, she leaned closer to listen to him purr.

"You not only *sing* your songs, Jenny," her grandmother went on. "You *feel* them. The people who hear you feel them. You make them want to be good. You may find this hard to understand, but as I have often said, I believe your voice is a gift from God. I told your mother so last night."

Fru Lind had spent the night in her new flat, but Fru Tengmark expected her to return any minute. Jenny had hurried up to the Widows' Home right after breakfast.

"What did the count say, Mormor?" she begged. "Mama said she would tell me this morning."

"You will have to know, I suppose, whatever is decided. You have been paid a great compliment, Jenny, but probably nothing will come of it. I do not believe that your mother will ever consent. She will never let you do it, and I understand how she feels."

"Do what? What did the count say?" Jenny repeated.

What the count had said was almost too wonderful to be believed. He said that Jenny had a remarkable voice, and one day Sweden would be proud of her. At that time, the Royal Opera, the Royal Theater, and the School for Pupils were all in the same building. The school, where talented young people could be trained for the stage, usually did not admit girls under fourteen. But the count had suggested that Jenny be enrolled at once as an actress-pupil. She would be taught to act and dance — *and sing.* All her expenses would be paid by the Swedish government.

Jenny went over and stood by her grandmother's chair.

"Why do you say that I can't do it?" she asked. "I want to learn to sing — more than anything in the world."

"I know that, but your mother does not think the theater is the proper place for an eight-year-old girl."

"I'll be nine in October."

"Yes, *lillen,* and I do not like to see you disappointed. But I had to tell your mother that I agreed with her."

Fru Lind came in. She took off her bonnet and sat down on the sofa. Kisse Katt jumped down and stalked across the room, his tail held high. Fru Lind paid no attention.

"I lay awake all night," she said, "trying to decide if I should accept the count's offer."

"Jenny's education would be taken care of," said Fru Tengmark thoughtfully. "Herr Andersson and his wife love the child, but they are poor. They can do nothing more for her."

"The count also suggested," Fru Lind went on, "that several of the other pupils could live with me, and the school would pay me to take care of them. But people in the theater are so wicked."

Jenny wrinkled her forehead, trying to understand. Why should Mama talk that way? Mademoiselle Lundberg and Herr Croelius were in the theater, and they were good and kind. She was sure that the count wasn't wicked, either. He was cross, but that was different.

"I wouldn't be wicked, Mama," Jenny promised. "Truly I wouldn't."

Fru Tengmark could not help smiling.

"The child is right," she said. "Jenny has had a good religious training. I believe she would be a good girl no matter where she went."

"Yesterday, you said — "

"I know what I said yesterday," Fru Tengmark interrupted, "but I too have been thinking about the count. He has made you a remarkable offer. It is true that I have not approved of the theater, but that may be because I have never been inside one. We often disapprove of things we do not know anything about, and we must not let our prejudice stand in the way of Jenny's welfare."

"But to let her go on the stage — to sacrifice my own child to the stage!" said Fru Lind uncertainly.

"Are you sure that it would be a sacrifice?" Fru Tengmark went on. "Is it right that a few of us here should be the only ones to enjoy our Jenny's songs? We should be willing to share a voice like hers with others. Thousands of people would be better men and women for having heard our Jenny sing."

There was a long silence. Fru Lind sighed.

"Perhaps it would not be right," she said finally, "to keep the child's talent just for ourselves. I shall go to see the count this afternoon."

The color came back to Jenny's cheeks. She was going to learn to sing — to really sing!

"I believe you have made a wise decision, daughter," said Fru Tengmark. "You know what I told you when Jenny was only four — that she would bring you help."

Fru Lind nodded. She too was thinking of the day when a small Jenny had heard a bugler play a fanfare, then picked out exactly the same notes on the piano. The child had talent, certainly. Also, the money the count had offered to pay Fru Lind would be most welcome.

"I hope that I am doing right," she said.

When Fru Andersson heard the good news, she baked some ginger cookies for the afternoon coffee hour, and several of Mormor's friends met in her sitting room to help Jenny celebrate. Fru Larsen felt very proud when she learned that Jenny had sung one of the songs that she had taught her — a song from opera at that. No wonder, the old lady boasted, that Herr Music Master and Herr Director had been impressed.

"Jenny," she added, "you are just like Askungen."

Askungen was the Swedish name for Cinderella. Jenny clapped her hands in delight.

"Then every one of you must be a fairy godmother, because all of you have been so good to me."

At that moment Kisse Katt decided to catch an imaginary mouse. He raced across the floor. He whirled around and chased his tail. He rolled over on his back and waved four white paws in the air. Fru Larsen reached over and tickled him under the chin.

"Jenny," she said, "I believe even your pussy is pleased, and don't forget that he deserves some of the credit. If you had not sung to him so often, Mademoiselle Lundberg's maid might never have heard you."

"You are right," said Fru Andersson, and she began to laugh. "When our *lillen* becomes famous, perhaps the story will be told of how she began by singing to her cat and how her cat loved to listen to her."

Fru Andersson and Fru Tengmark exchanged glances. Both were remembering the shy, frightened child, eager to love and to be loved, who had arrived nearly a year before. Since then Kisse Katt had been her constant companion, and in the warmth of her pet's affection she had grown more confident, more sure of

herself. Yes, Jenny Lind owed much to Kisse Katt.

That night Jenny was allowed to stay up late. She sat on the sofa with her pet as she listened to her mother and grandmother making plans for the future.

"Ah, I shall miss the child," said Fru Tengmark.

Jenny looked at her in alarm.

"I'll still live here, won't I?" she asked. "I can walk to the Opera House every day. I am big enough to go alone."

"Don't be silly!" said Fru Lind. "You will live at home with me. That is part of the plan. You are one of the pupils I am to take care of, and the theater will pay me."

Jenny ran across the room and threw herself into her grandmother's arms.

"Oh, Mormor, I don't want to leave you ever," she sobbed. "I want to learn to sing, but why can't I stay here? I won't go — I won't — "

Fru Tengmark held her close.

"There, there! We shall miss each other, but we must be brave. Remember, you are going to be a great singer. What is even more important, my darling, you are going to be a great, good woman."

Jenny closed her eyes tight, but a few tears squeezed through.

"Besides," Mormor went on, trying to sound cheerful, "you will have Kisse Katt to comfort you."

"Indeed she won't," said Fru Lind. "I am not going

to have any cats getting under foot around *my* house."

Kisse Katt was never one to keep his opinions to himself. He rose and arched his back. Every gray hair, every white hair bristled, until he seemed twice his usual size. His tail threshed back and forth.

"Psst!" he said.

Fru Tengmark smiled, then tried to hide the smile.

"Do not be too hard on the child. She will miss her pet."

"Jenny will be too busy to think of such nonsense," snapped Fru Lind.

"Don't you worry about Kisse Katt," Mormor said to Jenny. "I'll look after him."

After Jenny was in bed, she lay for a long time staring into the shadows. It was a strange feeling — to be both glad and sorry. The tears spilled over on her pillow and she thought of leaving her beloved Kisse Katt and this place where she had been so happy. At the same time, she wanted to go. She wanted to learn the right way to use the precious voice that Mormor said was a gift from God. But why couldn't she stay here while she was learning to sing? Why must a choice be made?

At that moment there was a gentle thud, as Kisse Katt jumped up on the bed, purring a soft good night. It was too dark really to see him, yet she knew exactly how he looked. His eyes were half closed. There was a blissful, contented expression on that little gray face as he arched his head in the hollow of her hand. Suddenly she remembered the northern lights. Mormor had said one could always keep the memory of a lovely thing.

"Kisse Katt," she told him, "when I get lonely, I'll close my eyes and think about you very hard."

Her pet answered with a sleepy purr and settled down at the foot of the bed to spend the night.

Jenny's First Play

THE SCHOOL FOR PUPILS was on the second floor of the handsome Opera House. The first person Jenny met was the French matron, Mademoiselle Bayard, who looked after the girls and young ladies studying to go on the stage. A big black cat lay asleep in her lap. Jenny was delighted.

"You have a Kisse Katt too!" she said.

"*Oui!* This is Monsieur Chat," Mademoiselle replied, using the French words for "Mr. Cat." "He is my own special pet, but you may see others too. Every theater has cats, you know. They bring good luck — especially black ones."

"My Kisse Katt is gray," said Jenny defensively, "and he brought me good luck."

"*Certainement, ma chère! All* cats bring good luck, whatever their color may be."

"Really?" Jenny asked.

Mademoiselle shrugged.

"Who knows? There are some who say it is a superstition, but it is what we in the theater like to believe. It is a good belief, *n'est-ce-pas?* It gives us confidence — makes us less afraid to go out on that big stage and dance or act or sing before all those hundreds of people."

Jenny's knees suddenly felt weak. Much as she liked to sing, it had not occurred to her that someday she would be expected to sing before hundreds of people all at the same time. She did not know how she could ever find the courage, and she reached out a trembling hand to stroke Monsieur Chat. His black fur felt like velvet under her fingers. He was very handsome.

But he wasn't Kisse Katt, she thought sadly. She missed her own dear pet.

Mademoiselle rose and led the way down the hall. In one of the studios three girls were waiting. They wore the uniform of the school — a plain black dress exactly like the one that had been given to Jenny. Mademoiselle introduced them as the actress-pupils who were to room and board with Fru Lind.

Charlotte and Mathilda Ficker were sisters, about fourteen and fifteen, with blue eyes and neat brown braids. The third girl, Fanny Westerdahl, looked at least sixteen. She was pretty and confident, as though she knew that one day she would be a famous actress. She put her arm around Jenny's shoulders.

"I think I shall like living with you," she said. "It will seem like having my little sister here with me."

The next year was a happy one for Jenny. Her singing masters — Herr Croelius and, later, Herr Berg — often praised her, but she knew that having a good voice was not enough. She must learn the right way to use it. Hour after hour, day after day, Jenny practiced her scales and exercises.

Singing lessons took only part of her time. She also studied piano and French, and she was taught to dance and to act. About a month after her tenth birthday she played her first part on a real stage. She was Angela in a play called *The Polish Mine — A Drama with Dancing*. She had rehearsed it many times, but on the night of the first performance she was really frightened.

What if she forgot her lines?

What if she forgot her dance steps?

What if the audience did not like her?

Out on the stage, the scenery for the first act was in place. It showed the great hall of a castle belonging to a wicked tyrant. The child Angela and her mother were prisoners, and Angela's father had come there in disguise to try to rescue them. Angela had been asked to dance for the tyrant's guests, and when she saw her father she cried out in surprise. To her dismay, she realized that she had betrayed his secret.

The next scene showed a dungeon, into which all three had been thrown. The play became very exciting when Jenny, as Angela, persuaded the warden to give her the key. Jenny was so interested in helping Angela's parents escape that she forgot everything else. She forgot to be afraid. She forgot that she was Jenny Lind. Not until the curtain fell for the last time, and there was a roar of applause from the audience, did she remember where and who she was.

It turned out to be a busy winter for a ten-year-old girl. She continued her music lessons during the day and frequently acted in plays at night. The following March found her rehearsing the part of Johanna in a play called *The Will.* Jenny was overjoyed when the directors of the theater gave her three tickets for the night of the opening performance. Her father had returned to Stockholm for a time, and two of the tickets were for her parents. The third she sent to her beloved Mormor. She did so want to make them proud of her.

After the curtain fell on the last act, all three went backstage to see Jenny. Even Fru Lind seemed pleased. Niclas Lind hugged his daughter in an embrace that left her breathless. Fru Tengmark's eyes were brimming with proud and happy tears.

"It is a long time since you have been to see us," she reminded her granddaughter. "But I know how busy you have been."

"Oh, Mormor, I will come," Jenny promised. "I will come soon."

Lessons and rehearsals left little time for visiting, but the following week Jenny obtained permission from her teachers to spend an afternoon at the Widows' Home. She stopped first at the lodge by the gate where she was greeted warmly by the steward and his wife. Kisse Katt was not there. Fru Andersson explained that he spent most of his time with Fru Tengmark. She and the other old ladies rather spoiled him, often giving him the cream they should have used in their coffee.

"In spite of all the attention, he misses you, Jenny," Fru Andersson assured her. "He still likes you best."

"Thank you, *Tant*," said Jenny. "I must go to see Mormor now, but I'll be back."

She found Fru Tengmark knitting in her favorite chair in a patch of sunlight by the window. Kisse Katt was in her lap, but with a glad little mew he jumped down and bounded across the floor. Jenny leaned down to pat him even before she kissed her grandmother. Then she and Kisse Katt sat together on the sofa. The gray cat rubbed against her, and when she tickled him behind the ears he arched his head in the hollow of her hand.

Fru Tengmark picked up her knitting again.

"I was very proud of you the other night," she said. "Did you read what the Stockholm newspaper said of your performance? No? Well, I have been saving it to show you."

She picked up the newspaper and read aloud:

> Jenny Lind . . . only ten or eleven years old, shows in her acting a quick perception, a fire and feeling, far beyond her years, which seem to denote an uncommon disposition for the theater.

Jenny flushed.

"Oh, Mormor," she said, "I have so much to learn. People are so good to me. When they praise me, I know I must work harder than ever. I want to make myself worthy of their praise."

"That is the way I like to hear my Jenny talk! But tell me, why are you not allowed to sing?"

"I take a singing lesson nearly every day," Jenny replied. "Herr Berg has promised that soon I may sing duets with him."

"In opera?"

"No, in private concerts at the houses of his friends. But I shall sing in opera someday, if I work hard, he says. I do so want to be a great singer."

"And a great, good woman. Don't forget that, Jenny."

"I shall try," said Jenny humbly.

"In the meantime," — Fru Tengmark's lips twitched in a smile — "are you being a good girl? Have you learned to be more patient with your mother?"

Jenny shook her head.

"Not always. Mama finds it very hard work to cook and sew and wash and iron for four of us. I don't always remember that when she gets cross. Fanny told me — "

Jenny hesitated.

"What is it that troubles you, dear?" asked Fru Tengmark.

"Well, Fanny said that she and Charlotte and Mathilda are going to ask Mademoiselle to let them live at the school. They think that Mama is too strict. I shall be so lonely without them."

"Patience, *lillen!* Remember what the Good Book says: 'A merry heart doeth good like a medicine.' "

An understanding smile passed between them. Kisse Katt stood on his hind legs and nuzzled his head just under Jenny's chin.

"Listen to him purr," she said.

Fru Tengmark laughed softly.

"He has been purring like that every since I told him how well you did in the play the other night."

Jenny held him close.

"I knew you wouldn't forget me, Kisse Katt," she told him, "and I'll never, *never* forget you."

Pictures in the Clouds

JENNY HAD KNOWN from the time Kisse Katt first came that they would not always have him. Mormor had warned her, but when she learned that he had died, she ran all the way to school, where she knew Mademoiselle Bayard would understand.

"*Oui, ma chère*. I do know how you feel." The kindly matron placed her arm around Jenny's shoulders and drew her close. "But our pets cannot live as long as we who love them. We have their friendship for a while, and we must be happy in the memory of their love and devotion. One must have courage, *n'est-ce-pas?*"

Jenny straightened. It was time for her singing lesson, and she must not keep Herr Berg waiting. . . .

Some months later she found it even harder to be brave. The year she was thirteen, the good Fru Tengmark died. Jenny, closing her eyes, could still see her grandmother sitting in a sunny spot by the window, with Kisse Katt curled up on her lap. She could hear the sweet voice saying: "You are going to be a great singer, *lillen*. More important, you are going to be a great, good woman."

"I shall try," Jenny whispered, repeating her promise. She must — she would — live up to Mormor's expectations.

It wasn't always easy to be good. She was very lonely that next year. Fanny Westerdahl finally carried out her threat and left Fru Lind's flat, and persuaded Charlotte and Mathilda Ficker to go with her. Mademoiselle Bayard found rooms for them on an upper floor of the Opera House, and now she was looking after them at night as well as during the day. Jenny missed their evenings together.

"Jenny is unhappy," Charlotte told Mademoiselle one day in October, 1834. "Her mother is so cross with her."

"Fru Lind is cross with everyone," said Fanny, with a toss of her dark curls. "We ought to know. We stayed with her until we could not stand it any longer. It is so much nicer here with you, Mademoiselle."

Mathilda glanced around the big room.

"Yes, it would be perfect if Jenny were with us. I wish she could live here too."

As she spoke, there was the sound of running feet on the stairs. Jenny Lind stood in the doorway. At fourteen, she was several inches taller than when she had first sung for the count, but she was still the smallest girl in the school. She wore a red cape and bonnet, and she was carrying the rest of her clothes in a big bundle.

"Oh, Mademoiselle — " she began, then burst into tears.

"Let me have your cape and bonnet," said Mademoiselle Bayard. Turning to the others, she added in an undertone, "Leave me alone with her, *s'il vous plaît.*"

The three girls turned to leave, glancing back over their shoulders. Mademoiselle drew Jenny down beside her on the sofa.

"Now, *ma chère,* tell me what is wrong," she said.

"I have run away from home," Jenny confessed tearfully. "I love Mama. Truly I do, and sometimes she seems to love me. Then again — like today . . ."

Jenny buried her face on Mademoiselle's shoulder.

"I . . . I didn't set the table right away when Mama told me to. I was studying my French lesson, and I didn't hear her ask me. Mama shook me and boxed my ears. I'm too old to be treated that way. I won't, I won't! Please let me come here and live with you."

"Your parents might not like that."

"But Papa is hardly ever at home," said Jenny desperately. "Mama scolds me all the time, and she makes me so unhappy that I . . . I can't sing."

Mademoiselle rose determinedly. She had Jenny lie down on the sofa and covered her with a shawl.

"Now you must have some rest, *ma chère.* I shall report to the directors of the theater what you have told me. Perhaps it can be arranged for you to stay here."

"I am so lonely," said Jenny wistfully. "Why can't I have a happy home like other girls?"

Mademoiselle had no answer to that question. But she kept her promise and talked with the directors. They agreed that for Jenny's own good, and for the sake of her studies, she should be allowed to stay.

To this plan, Fru Lind made vigorous objection. She and her husband asked a judge in the Swedish law court to make Jenny come home. He thought it over carefully, then said that she could go on living at the school — for a while. Later he would decide what was best to do.

A year went by. Then more months passed, and Jenny's new happiness showed in her voice. It improved so much that in February, following her fifteenth birthday, she was given a small part in a new opera. Unfortunately, the opera was not a success, for the audience did not like it. There were only four performances, but Jenny's voice was warmly praised.

Meanwhile she had made new friends among the other pupils. Her best friend was Mina Fundin, who shared many of her hopes and dreams. On the evenings when Jenny was not acting in a play they attended the opera together. Their favorite opera was called *Der Freischütz* (*The Freeshooter*), and they saw it again and again. In the second act Agatha sits at her window in the moonlight and sings a prayer for her sweetheart. The music is sad but very beautiful, and Jenny liked to imagine herself singing the same song:

> Softly sighing,
> Day is dying,
> May my prayer reach to the sky. . . .

"Mina," she said one evening, "do you think I will ever sing well enough to take the part of Agatha?"

"Of course," said Mina loyally. "Didn't Herr Berg tell you that your voice improves with every lesson? Well, it should improve after the way you practice. None of us works as hard as you do."

Jenny did work hard. Part of the improvement in her voice, she realized, was because of her long hours of practice. There was also another reason. She always sang better when she was happy, and she was very happy at the school. She wished she could stay forever.

But that was not to be. One morning in June, 1836, she and Mademoiselle Bayard put on their shawls and bonnets, and met Fru Lind at the law court. Jenny and her mother stood before the judge while he asked them questions.

Fru Lind was pale. Her voice shook as she promised to be more patient. She begged the judge to let Jenny come home again to live. Jenny watched in surprise. Why, her mother really did love her!

The judge was looking at Jenny now.

"My child," he said, "I am going to send you home. I want you to remember that grown people often have troubles that younger people do not understand. Your mother has had a hard life, and you may have been a great trial to her at times. She has said that she will try to be more patient. Will you make me the same promise?"

Jenny swallowed hard.

"I . . . I promise," she said.

Her disappointment at leaving Mademoiselle Bayard and her friends at the school was made easier by this new and amazing knowledge about her mother. Fru Lind wanted and needed her, and that was enough for Jenny. She would do her best to be a good daughter.

After Jenny returned home, Fru Lind tried hard to be patient and to give her the love and understanding she had always wanted. In July the two of them left for a holiday in the country, and they took Mina with them. The girls forgot that they were almost grown up,

as they romped with the puppies and kittens on the farm at which they were staying. They had a picnic nearly every day, and there was a haystack where they could slide. When they were tired, they lay back against the sweet-smelling hay, daydreaming, as they watched the shifting clouds in a blue sky.

Jenny had a secret that she longed to share with Mina, but Herr Berg had asked her to tell no one for a while. As an actress-pupil she received only pocket money, but with the beginning of the next year, 1837 — which was only five months away — the directors had decided that she was to be a real actress. She was to be paid a real salary. At first it would be small, but she could begin to help her mother. In a few years she would earn more money, and then she knew exactly what she wanted to do.

As she looked up at the sky, she began to make pictures in the clouds. She seemed to see a little house — the kind of house she hoped to buy for her parents, so they could always be together.

The clouds shifted, and she saw another picture forming in the sky. She saw herself singing before a large audience. She was singing in *Der Freischütz.* The role of Agatha was usually given to a famous soprano, but someday . . . perhaps someday . . . Jenny could almost hear Agatha's words in the last act, when she sees her sweetheart returning:

How every pulse is flying,
And my heart beats loud and fast,
We shall meet in joy at last,
Yes, we shall meet in joy at last!

A Date To Remember

JENNY LIND WAS SIXTEEN when she became a real actress with a real salary, and for another year she continued to act in plays. She also took singing lessons, just as she had before, and she sang in concerts with Herr Berg. At a concert given the following December, several performers from the Royal Opera House sang the music from one act of an opera in which Jenny took the part of a girl named Alice. Although she had only one song, she sang it so well that the audience cheered and applauded. Her cheeks were flushed when she came to the front of the platform and made a curtsy.

Afterward her friends gathered around her. The singing master beamed with pride.

"Jenny," he said, "the directors have decided to present *Der Freischütz* early next year. I am looking for the right singer for the role of Agatha. Be so good as to come to see me at my studio tomorrow morning."

As the door closed behind him, Jenny caught her breath.

"Did you hear what he said?" asked Mina. "Perhaps he intends to ask *you*."

"But only famous singers take the part of Agatha," Jenny protested. "It is such an important role. Am I ready for it?"

"After the way you sang tonight?" scoffed Fanny.

"It is my dearest wish to be Agatha," said Jenny simply. "But am I good enough?"

"Is she good enough?" Mina turned to Mathilda, trying to look solemn.

Mathilda turned to Fanny and repeated the question, but the words ended in a giggle.

Only Jenny looked serious.

"You needn't laugh. I know how much I still have to learn."

The next morning she arrived early at Herr Berg's studio. The door opened at once in answer to her knock. The singing master's dark eyes glowed behind his spectacles as he took her hand and led her to a chair.

"My child," he said, "for several years you have been a faithful pupil. You have studied hard. You have proved yourself a good actress, and your singing voice has grown in power and beauty."

"Thank you."

Jenny was sitting on the edge of the chair, her hands clasped tightly in her lap.

"Now you are to have your big chance."

Jenny swallowed hard.

"But I must not keep you in suspense," the singing master went on. "How would you like to sing regularly in opera? How would you like"—he paused—"to take the part of Agatha?"

"Oh, Herr Berg!" Surprisingly, Jenny burst into tears. "Excuse me for crying, but I am so happy. I . . . I hope I shall be worthy of your faith in me."

From the moment Jenny left the studio, she did not take time to remember how happy she was that her dearest wish was coming true. She thought only of the work ahead of her. Hour after hour, day after day, she practiced the part of Agatha. She knew every line of her role, and every note was perfect. At the final rehearsal she sang so well that the members of the orchestra laid down their instruments to applaud.

Jenny's first performance as Agatha was to take place on March 7, 1838. No one present at the Royal Opera House was every to forget that night. Backstage there was much rushing to and fro. Some of the men who were to take part in the opera paced back and forth, singing under their breath, going over their lines. The ladies sat before their dressing tables, powdering their noses, fixing their hair.

Now that Jenny was a star, she had a dressing room to herself. She was wearing the costume of Agatha, a Bohemian peasant girl — a white bodice over a blue-striped skirt that made her eyes look blue. At last she was to sing the part she had yearned to sing. But her face was hidden in her hands, and she was shaking all over. She did not see how she could possibly go out on that big stage and sing before all those hundreds of people. Never had she been so frightened.

Mademoiselle Bayard came in.

"Jenny," she cried out in distress. "The audience must not see you with your eyes red from weeping. Let me have your powder puff."

Jenny hastily dried her eyes.

"I am so ashamed, Mademoiselle, but I am so . . . so scared."

"It is just that you have stage fright," said Mademoiselle cheerfully. "Every performer is frightened before a performance, but the feeling will pass. Remember, this is to be the night of your great triumph."

"I . . . I hope so."

"Now I shall leave you alone," said Mademoiselle Bayard. "You do not have your first song until the second act. You have time to rest — to get hold of yourself. You must be calm."

Jenny did feel a little calmer as she turned back to

her dressing table. Then came a sound from out front that made her heart sink. The orchestra was tuning up!

The curtain was raised and the performers began to sing. Closing her eyes, she listened to every note of every song. She waited for the burst of applause as the first act ended.

Then came the noise of the scene shifters getting the stage ready for Act II. This showed Agatha's room. Jenny had only a few more minutes before she would have to walk out on that stage. She tried not to cry, but in spite of all she could do, the tears poured down her cheeks.

At that moment she felt something soft and furry rub against her ankles. She looked down. It was a cat — a handsome gray cat with white paws and a white shirt front. He leaped to the dressing table. He looked at her out of wide green eyes.

"Why, Kisse Katt!" she said, then stopped in confusion.

"You know," she went on, "you look exactly like my own darling Kisse Katt I had when I was a little girl."

She noticed that the cat was curling and uncurling his front paws, the way Kisse Katt had always done when he was pleased. She leaned closer to pet him, and he arched his head in the hollow of her hand. She tickled him behind the ears, and he began to purr. It was a reassuring kind of purr. She could almost imagine that he was purring words.

"Courage!" he seemed to be telling her. "Courage!"

Jenny stiffened.

"I must have courage," she said. "I will have — "

She interrupted by a knock.

"Time to go on," a voice called from the other side of her dressing-room door.

Jenny rose and smoothed her skirts. She looked down at the handsome cat. His purr sounded almost as loud as the kettledrums in the orchestra.

"Thank you, Kisse Katt," she whispered.

Several of Jenny's friends were waiting in the wings. Herr Berg, the singing master, was there. Charlotte and Mathilda and Fanny were there. Mina and Mademoiselle Bayard watched anxiously as Jenny walked out on the stage.

Her first number was a duet. She and the young woman who sang with her had a gay, sprightly song, and there was polite applause from the audience.

Next came Jenny's big scene — when Agatha prayed for her sweetheart. Hundreds of people were waiting to hear her sing that song. She seated herself by the window, her face very pale in the artificial moonlight. She took a deep breath and began:

> Softly sighing,
> Day is dying,
> May my prayer reach to the sky. . . .

With the first note something wonderful happened. Jenny forgot that she had ever been afraid. She forgot that the moonlight was not real. She forgot that she was Jenny Lind. She was Agatha now, and the song poured forth from her throat in a golden stream.

Everyone in the theater leaned forward to listen. They hardly seemed to breathe. A sigh, almost too small to be heard, went up at the last golden note died on the air.

A moment of silence was followed by a shout.

"*Brava!*" someone called.

"*Brava! Brava!* Jenny Lind!"

The audience was standing. The theater was shaken with cheers. Some of the people waved their handkerchiefs. Others used their handkerchiefs to dry their eyes. Jenny's song was so lovely, it had made them cry. Mademoiselle was crying. Mina and Fanny and Mathilda were crying. Herr Berg blew his nose.

That first song was the beginning of Jenny's triumph. After she finished her next number, there was another great burst of applause. When the opera was over, the curtains parted again, and Jenny walked to the front of the stage and made a curtsy. She was no longer plain. She was beautiful. The people out front were never to forget her radiant face. They began pelting her with flowers.

Her arms filled with blossoms, Jenny turned and beckoned to Herr Berg, standing in the wings. She

wanted him to share her triumph. He bowed over Jenny's hand. The two of them turned to the audience and bowed.

The applause swelled again, before the curtain fell for the last time.

Backstage, Jenny was overwhelmed with the good wishes of her friends. Mina and Fanny, Mathilda and Charlotte, hugged and kissed her. Finally Mademoiselle Bayard was able to lead her back to her dressing room. Outside the door, Jenny looked up with shining eyes.

"Ah, Mademoiselle," she said softly, "this morning I woke up one person, but tonight I shall go to bed quite another person. I know now what Mormor meant when she said that my voice was a gift from God. I have found my power."

"*Ma chère!*" Mademoiselle squeezed her hand.

A silence fell between them. Another voice spoke in Jenny's heart — a voice that only she could hear. How well she remembered the sweet low tones of Mormor when she said:

"You are going to be a great singer, Jenny. Even more important, my darling, you are going to be a great, good woman."

Jenny opened the door and went into her dressing room alone.

"Kisse Katt," she called softly.

The gray cat was not there.

She sank down on the stool before her dressing table.

It was almost as though she had imagined him, she thought. Memory was indeed a precious gift — a gift from God, Mormor would have said. She remembered Mormor's words long after they were spoken. She remembered the northern lights long after their brilliance had faded. Had it been the memory of Kisse Katt that had given her courage when she most needed it?

At that moment Jenny could not know that the sound of her voice was to linger long in the memory of those who heard her sing. She little guessed her triumph that evening was the first of many triumphs. But when she looked into her mirror, a seventeen-year-old girl looked back at her, a new confidence, a new wonder in her eyes.

Glossary

Swedish words and expressions used in this story of Jenny Lind, a real girl who lived in Stockholm, Sweden, include the following:

Askungen — the Swedish name for Cinderella
flicka — girl
Froken — Miss
Fru — Mrs.
Herr — Mr.
krona — a Swedish coin
Küngstradgarden — King's Park
lilla flicka — little girl
lillen — a pet name meaning "little one"
Mormor — mother's mother, or grandmother
Norrbro — North Bridge
Tant — Aunt or Aunty
Torg — place or square

Many people who lived in Stockholm during Jenny Lind's time also spoke French, and the following French words and expressions were often used:

ma chère — my dear
Madame — Mrs.
Mademoiselle — Miss
Monsieur — Mr.
oui — yes
n'est-ce-pas? — is it not so?
s'il vous plaît — if you please

From the Author

JENNY LIND became a great singer, famous throughout Europe as "the Swedish Nightingale." In 1850 she came to the United States, and a "Jenny Lind Fever" swept the country. She traveled from town to town, giving concerts, and it seemed that everyone wanted to hear her sing. Probably no star of stage, movies, or television is as popular now as Jenny Lind was then. Most of her earnings from the American tour she gave to charity; and her kindness, generosity, and charm made her as much loved for herself as for her voice.

America loved Jenny Lind, and Jenny Lind loved America. It was here she found her greatest happiness, for it was here she married and spent her honeymoon.

This story of Jenny Lind and her listening cat is based on true sources, including an account that Jenny gave her son years later. Her son wrote down what his mother had said. He did not mention the name of her pet, so in this story it is called Kisse Katt, which is Swedish for "kitty-cat." The steward and his wife who were so kind to Jenny have been called Herr and Fru Andersson because their real names have been forgotten. They were real persons, however, as were her beloved grandmother, her parents, her singing masters, and the friends she made at school.

The girl who sang her way into the hearts of thousands might well be called the "Cinderella of Song." But no one waved a magic wand for Jenny, as did Cinderella's godmother. Her remarkable voice and hard work furnished the magic. What her grandmother and her friends provided were love and understanding. Kisse Katt not only gave affection. He did even more. He set in motion the chain of events that brought about the discovery of Jenny's voice.

After Jenny Lind became one of the world's great singers, famous men and women were her friends. Kings and queens gave her costly presents. But she never forgot the people she had known when she was nine years old: Mormor who loved her, the friends who encouraged her, and the strangers who gave her her first great opportunity. Nor did she ever forget the little pet that had started her on her career. To the end of her life, Jenny Lind remembered Kisse Katt.